This book belongs to

____

For Azariah and Micah, my greatest blessings to date.

Published by TOC Publishing Ltd

Kemp House 152-160 City Road, London, EC1V 2NX

www.tocpublishing.com

ISBN 978-1-8381-6900-8

Wonderfully ME

Written by Toyin Owoseje

The sun was up, and the moon had gone to bed,
But Bisi didn't want to lift her head.
No cough or runny nose,
She just wanted to stay at home.

She said: "Mummy, I don't want to go to school.
All the other kids are just so cruel".

"They laugh at my brown skin and my hair curls,

And say I'm not pretty like the other girls.

They tease me when I dance and sing,

And say they don't like the lunches that I bring".

Mummy said: "My baby, you are the most beautiful girl,

I wished you believed what I know so well".

"Your rich brown skin tells a deep story,

Your black kinky hair is your crowning glory.

Your full pink lips make your dazzling smile,

Your cute button nose will never go out of style".

"You are mummy and daddy's perfect little superstar,

And we love you just the way you are.

When they laugh and say mean things,

Close your eyes and repeat after me".

"I am strong,
I am smart,
I am gorgeous,
And I have a big heart.
I am brave,
I am funny,
I am talented,
I am sweet like honey".

"My mummy loves me, and my daddy does too,
And because of all these reasons, I don't have to be like you.
I am the best person I can be,
Because I am wonderfully me".

When Bisi went to school she was no longer scared,
She felt brave because she remembered what her mummy said.

At breaktime Ben took her skipping rope in front of the whole class,

So many kids pointed and laughed.

But Bisi didn't cry or yell,
She knew her mummy's words so well.
She stood tall and said all the special things,
Her mummy had told her that morning.

"I am strong,
I am smart,
I am gorgeous,
And I have a big heart.
I am brave,
I am funny,
I am talented,
I am sweet like honey".

"My mummy loves me, and my daddy does too,
And because of all these reasons, I don't have to be like you.
I am the best person I can be,
Because I am wonderfully me".

At first Ben wanted to be unkind,
But then he changed his mind.
"I'm sorry for being mean," he said.
"You can be different and still be my friend".

That is when Bisi knew,
When you love yourself, it doesn't matter what others do.

From that day on, before Bisi went to school,
She always reminded herself that she was super cool.
She admired every dimple and curl,
And told herself the words she now knew so well.

"I am strong,
I am smart,
I am gorgeous,
And I have a big
heart.
I am brave,
I am funny,
I am talented,
I am sweet like honey".

"My mummy loves me, and my daddy does too,

And because of all these reasons, I don't have to be like you.

I am the best person I can be,

Because I am proud to be me".

Bisi
wants
you to
remember...

You are a good friend

You can be anything if you work hard

You will get better the more you practise

You are unique
and special

You are valued and loved

Colouring activity
01
02
03
04
05
06
07
08
09
10
11
12
13
14
15
16
17
18
19
20
21
22
23
24
25
26
27
28
29
30
31
32
33
34
35
36
37
38
39
40
41
42
43
44
45
46
47
48
49
50
51
52
53
54
55
56
57
58
59
60
61
62
63
64
65
66
67
68
69
70